A MESSAGE FROM
THE HEAD OF THE C.I.A.

Up to now, knowledge of the hilarity and inventiveness of "Spy vs. Spy" material has been "TOP SECRET" and "RESTRICTED" to readers of MAD. This book contains all-new and original material which is being leaked to the public for the first time. So watch yourself—you may die laughing.

Al Feldstein
Editor of MAD
and Head of the
Committee for
Idiotic Amusement

MAD'S

SPY vs SPY

by
ANTONIO PROHIAS

WARNER BOOKS

A Warner Communications Company

Antonio Prohias is a famous Cuban artist who defied the censorship of the Castro regime with anti-Communist cartoons until he was forced to flee Havana with his life. His first work in the U. S. A. was with MAD Magazine, where he was enthusiastically received along with his new, original and inventive "Spy Vs. Spy" cartoon feature.

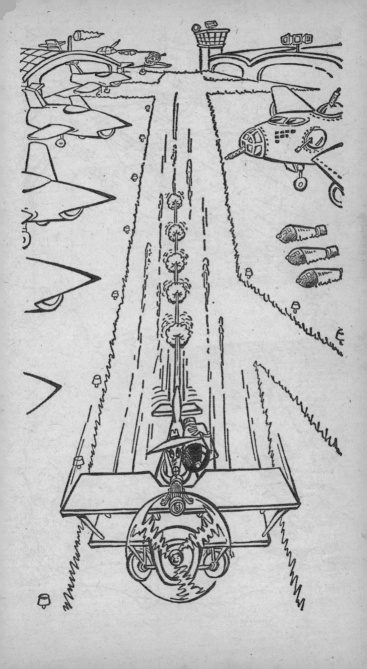

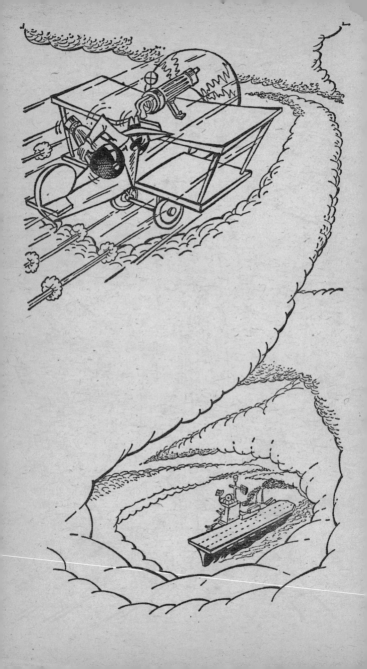

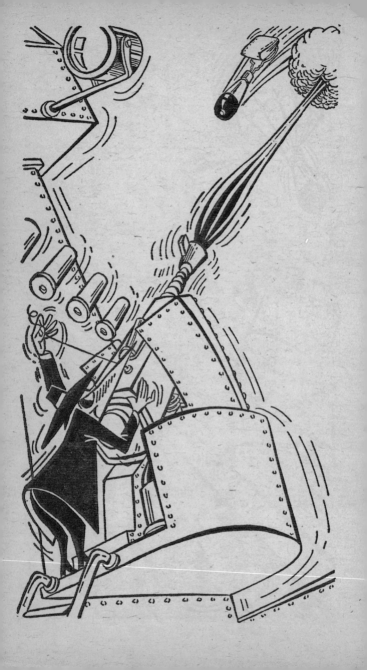

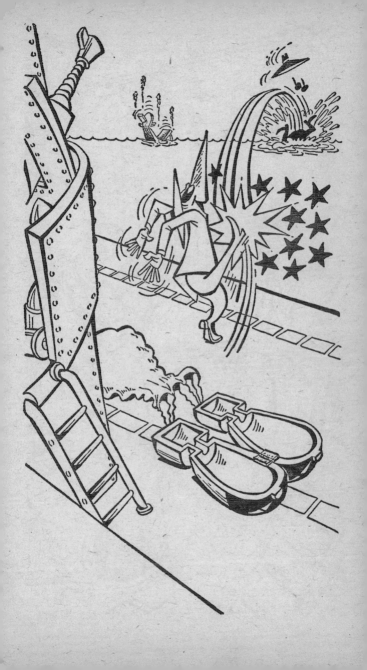

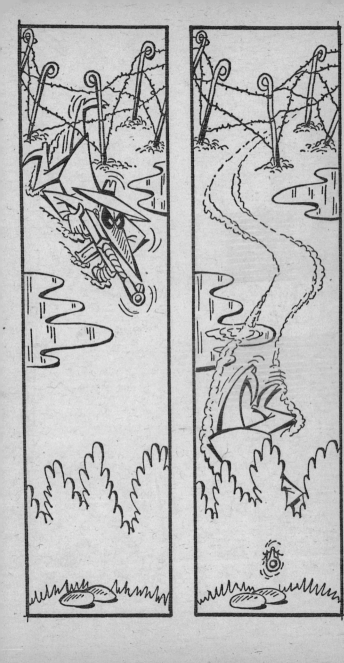

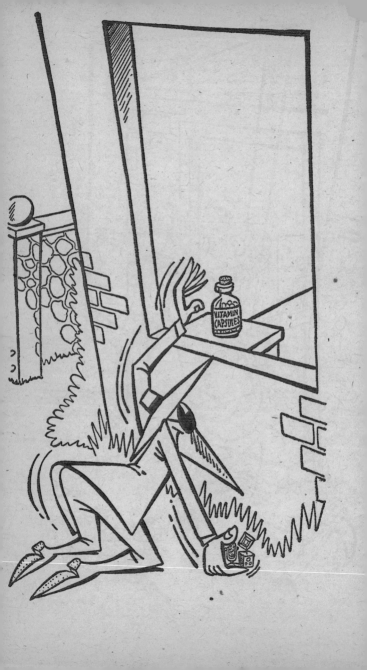

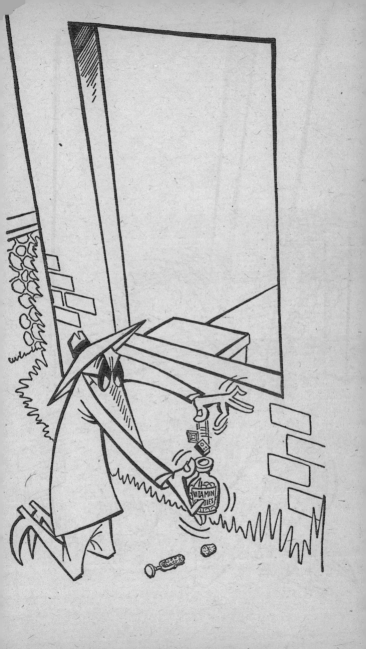

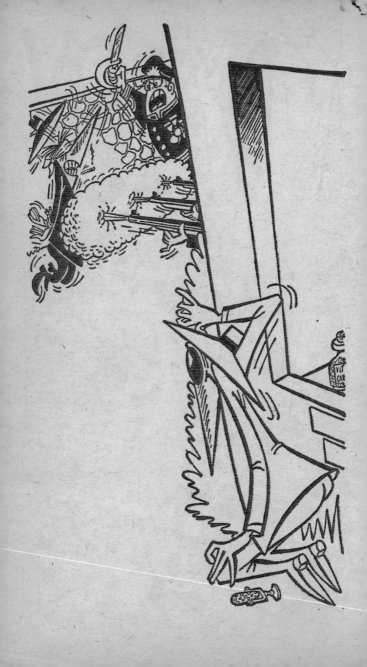

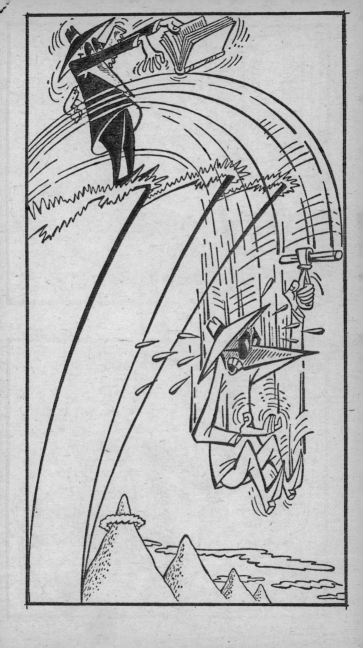

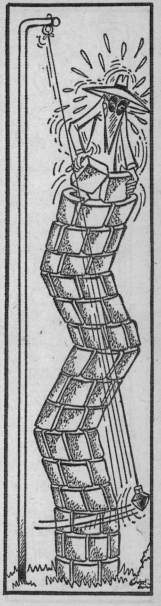

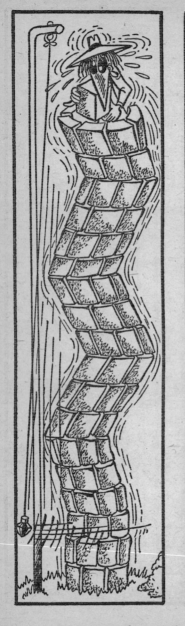

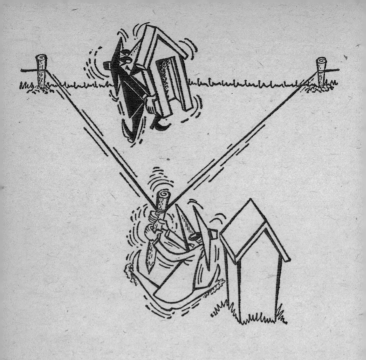

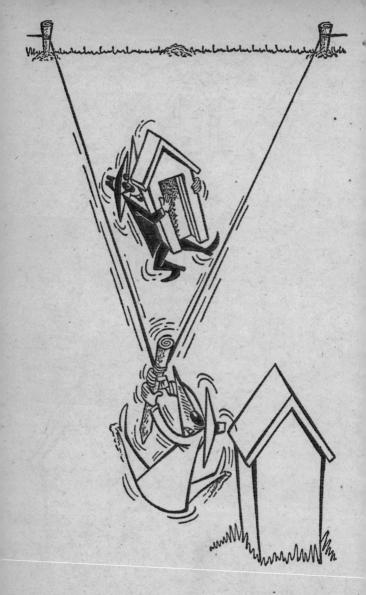

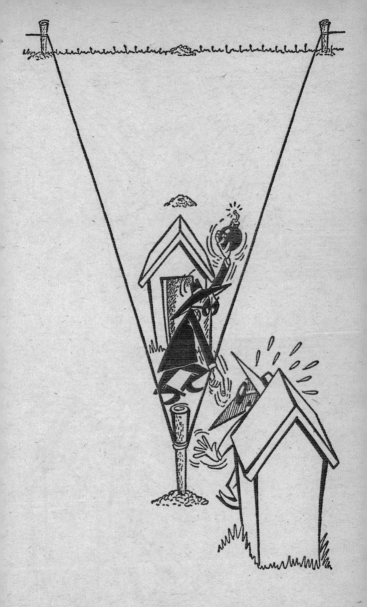

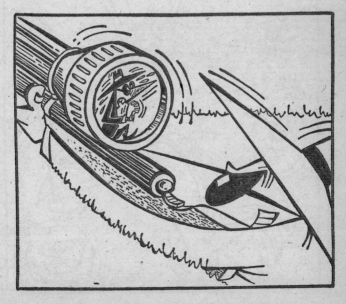

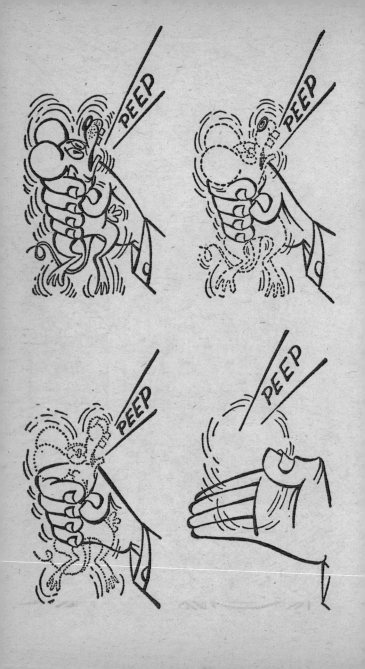

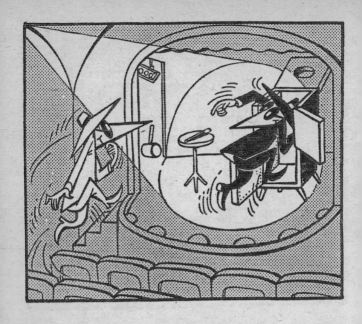

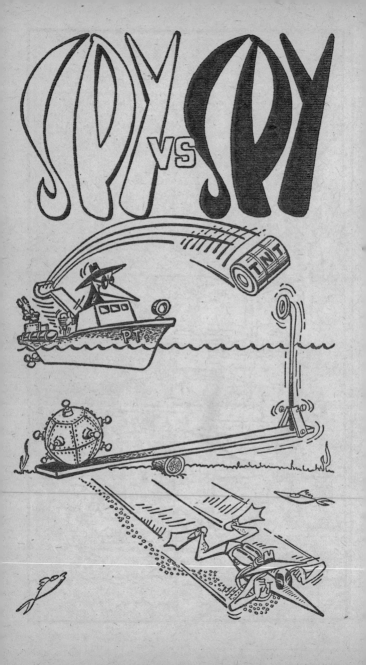

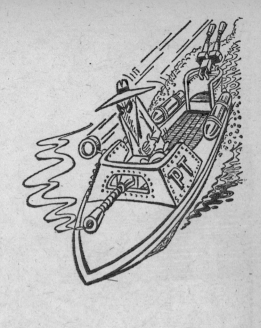

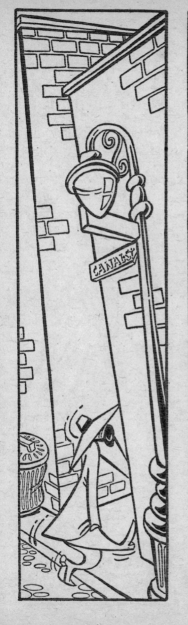

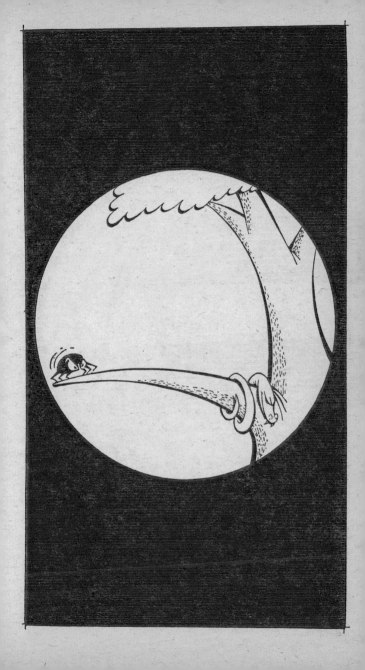

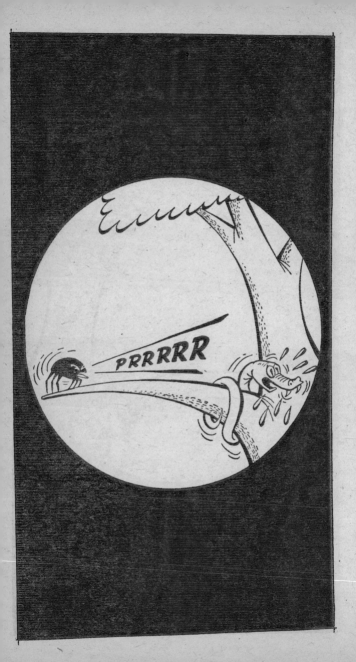

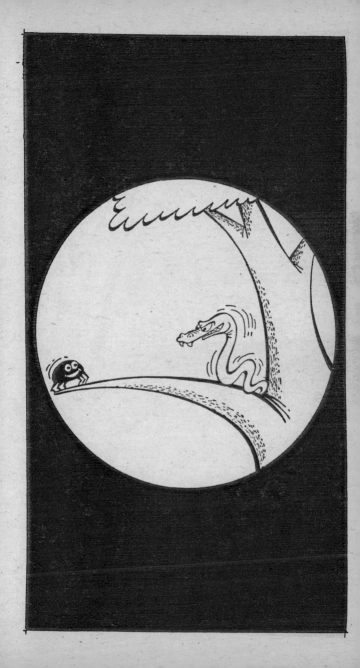

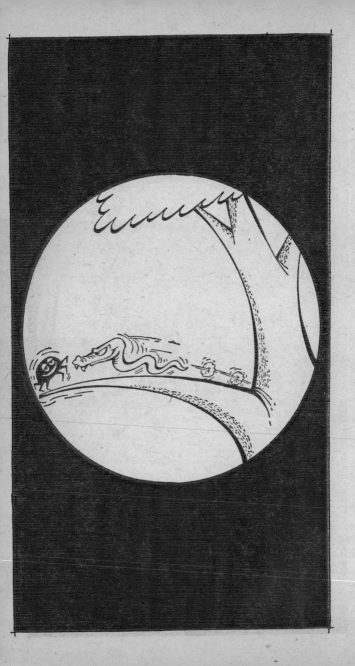

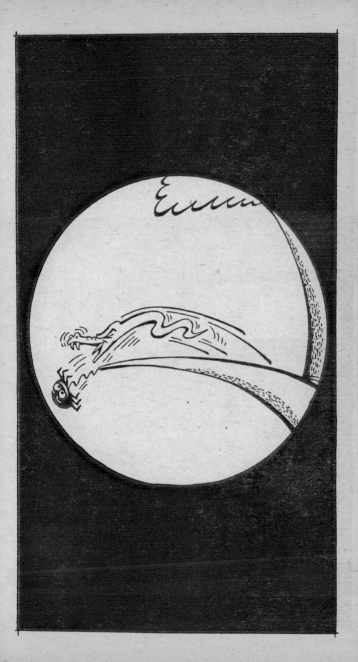

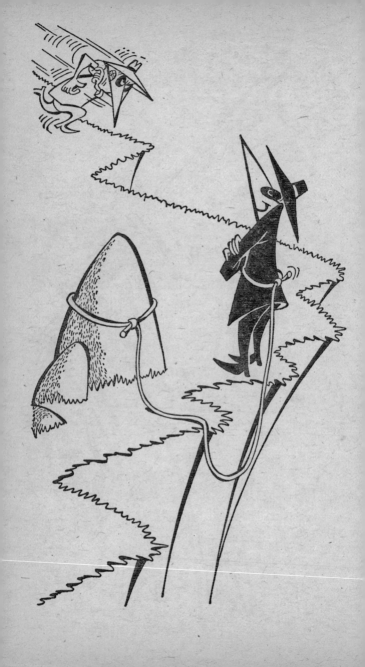

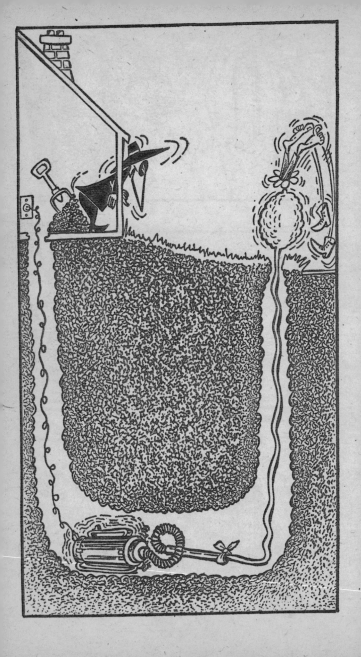

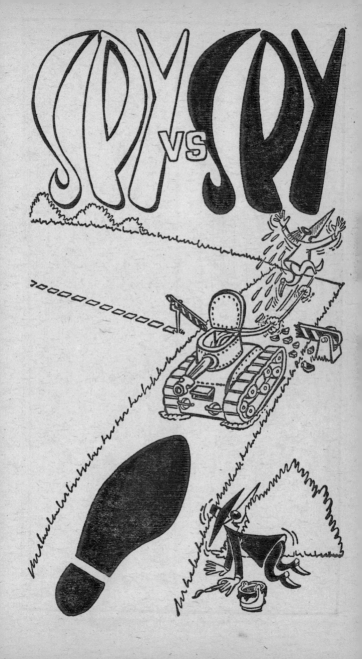

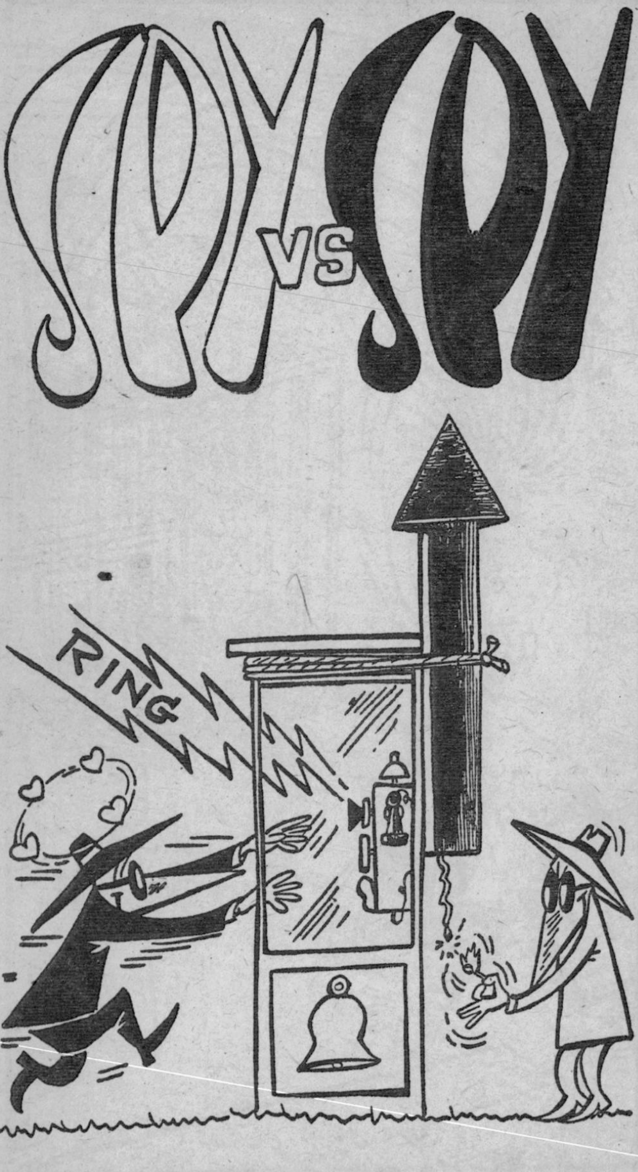
SPY vs SPY
RING

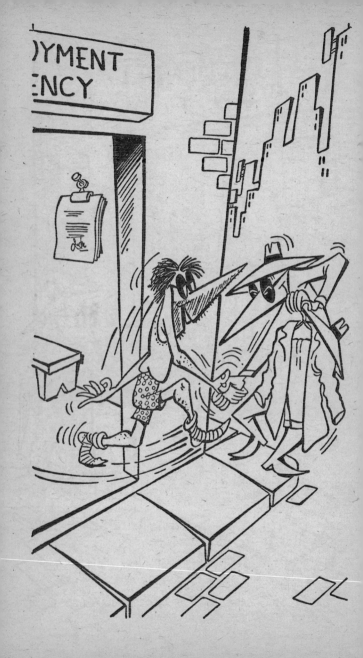